"Time for food!" chants Fern.
She looks in the barn on her farm.

In the barn on her farm are
three pigs.
Fern feeds them in the yard.

She feeds them corn cobs or slop.
The three pigs run fast for the food!

"Time for more food!" chants Fern.
She looks in the barn on her farm.
In the barn on her farm are hens
and chicks.

4

Fern feeds them in the yard.

She feeds them seeds or corn.

The hens hunt or peck for the food.

"Time for more food!" chants Fern.
She looks in the barn on her farm.
In the barn on her farm are
four sheep.

The four sheep trot into the yard.
They graze where they see
green grass.
They chomp, chomp, chomp.

"Time for food!" chants Fern.

Fern looks in the yard on her farm.

"Time for mine!" chants Fern.